Understanding behaviour

Fiona May
NAS Autism Helpline

Contents

Introduction

This booklet is intended to provide a basic overview of some of the behavioural difficulties that may be experienced by a person with an autistic spectrum disorder (ASD), as well as general guidelines on how to respond to these. Behavioural difficulties can be experienced by many people on the autistic spectrum, regardless of age or level of ability. Not all the information or approaches mentioned here will be relevant or appropriate for everyone, so it is important to bear in mind that each person and situation is unique. It is also important to think about how the issues raised relate to your own child, friend, family member and so on. You might find it useful to keep a note of any particular ideas and strategies that are especially relevant to your individual situation as you read through this booklet.

For more in-depth information, consult the books listed in the recommended reading section at the end of this booklet or call The National Autistic Society (NAS) Autism Helpline on 0845 070 4004. For complicated or serious behavioural difficulties – that is, behaviour that involves risk of harm to the person with autism, yourself or others – you should consult a specialist. Information on how and where to find specialist support is also to be found towards the end of this booklet on page 48.

Overview of difficulties affecting people with an ASD

There are many ways in which someone with an ASD can experience difficulties in making sense of the world and relating to others. An important step in understanding behaviour is that of gaining a clear understanding of these difficulties and, more specifically, how each person is affected by them as an individual.

The following section provides a summary of the main areas of difficulty associated with ASD and how these may affect an individual's behaviour.

Autism and Asperger syndrome are seen as belonging on a spectrum, with varying levels of difficulty experienced according to where an individual is on it. Some experience significant difficulty and have a learning disability or very high support needs, while others are of average or above average intelligence and experience difficulties that seem more subtle but are nevertheless still significant. No two individuals on the spectrum are the same. However, all will experience some degree of difficulty in areas known as the triad of impairments, as discussed on the following pages.

The triad of impairments
Communication

A broad range of communication difficulties can be experienced, involving both expressive (communicating with others) and receptive (understanding what others are communicating) areas. Some people on the spectrum never develop speech. Others do not have functional speech, but, rather, 'echo' the language of others. Language is often delayed and its development may follow a different pattern from that of other children.

Those who develop speech may find it difficult to use language effectively to communicate with others. Their speech may sometimes seem overly formal and the intonation and inflection of words can appear unnatural. For example, they may speak in a monotone voice and not stress certain words to convey the meaning of their message. They may have difficulties with using non-verbal communication (such as eye contact, facial expression and gestures) appropriately themselves and also decoding the body language of others properly.

Frequently, they have problems understanding speech. Some understand no speech at all and so do not respond to verbal information. Others understand parts of speech, but may have a very concrete or literal understanding of language and, as a result, find it hard or impossible to understand metaphors, turns of phrase or jokes used in everyday conversation. "Don't bite my head off," for example, may be very confusing or, indeed, worrying for some people with an ASD.

How these difficulties may be expressed behaviourally

- An inability to communicate wants and needs to others (such as pain, hunger, thirst, discomfort and frustration) can lead to the development of particular behaviour as an alternative means of communication.

- Difficulties with understanding the verbal information provided by others can lead to frustration, anxiety and confusion. This can be further exacerbated by others' reactions to their perceived lack of compliance to a request or instruction.

- Problems interpreting non-verbal information, such as facial expressions and body language, can create misunderstandings, which in turn may lead to behavioural difficulties.

- A very literal way of interpreting language and concrete thinking can create confusion and distress when they try to understand the language of others and can lead to behaviour that appears inappropriate.

Social interaction

All people with an ASD will experience some degree of difficulty engaging with others in reciprocal – two-way – social interactions. People with greater levels of difficulty may appear aloof or disinterested in others. They may not seek out contact with others and can seem disinterested in their peers. Others passively accept the contact of others but rarely initiate or seek out social contact.

Those at the higher functioning end of the spectrum may seek out social contact, but have difficulties doing this in an appropriate way. They may be unaware of the social rules of a particular situation and not understand the perspectives of other people. Interactions can be one-sided as the individual is unaware of the rules of conversation.

How these difficulties may be expressed behaviourally

- Social situations can be very unpredictable and stressful for people with an ASD, so an individual may engage in particular types of behaviour in order to avoid or limit social contact.

- Not understanding the importance of social interaction in meeting needs and wants can lead to behavioural difficulties as compensation.

- A lack of understanding of social rules can cause confusion and misunderstandings in social situations and may lead to behaviour that appears inappropriate to others.

Social imagination

Difficulties in this area may present in a number of ways. For example, young children may not develop the usual pretend play or imagination; others may be extremely creative or imaginative, but only when it comes to their area of special interest and never in relation to social situations. There is a tendency for individuals to focus in on the details of an object rather than the bigger picture – looking at the wheels of a car, rather than playing with the whole car, for example.

Many people experience a strong preference for routine and predictability and can become very distressed when unexpected changes occur. Thus, some people may develop a fascination with a particular object or activity and find it very difficult when this is not available to them. Others may engage in repetitive activities, such as hand flapping, rocking or spinning objects. People at the higher functioning end of the spectrum may develop special interests in a particular subject or topic.

Most individuals will also experience difficulties imagining things from another's perspective and understanding that another person may have feelings and thoughts that are different from their own. Many experience difficulties in planning, picturing what comes next in a sequence of tasks and understanding abstract concepts, such as the passage of time.

How these difficulties may be expressed behaviourally

- Changes to routine, unexpected events and unstructured time can cause extreme distress and may lead to behavioural difficulties, which are the individual's attempts to cope with these changes.

- Sequencing problems can make it very difficult to predict what is coming next, which can cause high levels of stress and anxiety.

- The inability to imagine events occurring in the future and difficulties understanding abstract concepts, such as the passage of time, can cause difficulties with waiting and behavioural issues may occur as a result of this lack of understanding.

- The individual may engage in behaviour that appears inappropriate, selfish or harmful due to difficulties in understanding the perspectives of others.

- Interruptions to activities of special interest can cause distress, leading to behavioural issues.

- A strong focus on areas of special interest can limit involvement in other activities and so affect the learning of new skills, which may, in turn, cause more problems socially.

Other difficulties

Sensory difficulties

Everyone receives information from the environment via the senses, which include visual (sight), auditory (sound), olfactory (smell), gustatory (taste), tactile (touch), vestibular (balance) and proprioceptive (body in space) systems. Many people with an ASD experience some form of sensory difficulty or dysfunction that appears to be related to how sensory information is processed in the brain. These difficulties may present as deficits, excesses or imbalances in one or more of the sensory systems and can impact significantly on how the individual experiences his or her world.

How these difficulties may be expressed behaviourally

- Overstimulation of one or more of the sensory systems can cause extreme agitation, anxiety and confusion and may lead to behavioural outbursts as an attempt to deal with this discomfort.

- Understimulation of one or more of the sensory systems can lead to behaviour that attempts to reinstate balance. Self-stimulatory or repetitive behaviour – such as spinning, jumping or flicking of objects – may be an attempt to gain input for a particular sensory system.

- Hyposensitivity (lack of sensitivity) of the tactile system may result in an increased tolerance of heat and pain.

Motor difficulties

Some people with an ASD experience difficulties with fine or gross motor co-ordination and control (controlling how the body moves). For example, they may have an odd posture or springy tiptoe walk. Some individuals may appear clumsy and have difficulty differentiating between left and right and up and down.

How these difficulties may be expressed behaviourally

- Clumsy or unusual motor responses can lead to difficulties in peer relationships and may be misunderstood as attention-seeking behaviour.

- Research suggests that some types of self-injury and aggressive behaviour may be features of tic disorders or compulsions. It has also been suggested that high levels of stress can increase the frequency of uncontrolled movements (Clements and Zarkowska, 2000).

Understanding the functions of behaviour

When thinking about a particular behavioural difficulty, it is important to ask the question, "What is the person trying to tell me by their behaviour?" and to think about the function that the behaviour has for the person as an individual. Identifying this aspect of a particular behaviour involves looking at what the person gains or avoids from engaging in that behaviour.

For an individual with an ASD, it is important to think about the triad of impairments (see page 3) and how they may be contributing to the behaviour. Bear the following questions in mind when thinking about the function of a particular behaviour.

- Is the person experiencing any pain, illness or physical discomfort, such as toothache, earache, digestion problems, allergies, seizures?

- How does the person communicate their needs, wants, feelings? Could the behaviour be a way of compensating for communication difficulties?

- Have there been any recent changes in the individual's life? For example, a new teacher, moving house, disruption to the usual routine?

- Are the person's obsessions, special interests or repetitive behaviour contributing to the behavioural difficulties?

- Is the person experiencing any sensory issues that may be affecting their behaviour?

- Is the behaviour related to problems with social understanding?

Sometimes a particular behaviour can have more than one function. Trying to communicate a want or need can come out as an attempt to gain attention of some sort or to bring about a particular outcome as a result of others' reactions and the individual's subsequent learning.

It is therefore important to understand the different factors that may be involved in triggering and maintaining a particular behaviour. Gathering together these behavioural clues and developing a hypothesis or theory to explain why a behaviour is occurring is called a functional analysis.

To complete such an analysis, we need to gather information about what happens before, during and after a behavioural incident and understand any relevant background factors that may be contributing to the behavioural difficulty. From this information, we are then able to establish whether or not there are any patterns and can form a hypothesis as to why the behaviour is occurring. For this reason it is important to keep track of behavioural incidents by recording what happens before, during and after an incident.

Recording behaviour

Behavioural records as shown below are often referred to as 'ABC' charts. 'A' in this instance stands for 'antecedents' – that is, what occurs immediately before the behavioural outburst – and includes any triggers, signs of distress or environmental information. The 'B' refers to the 'behaviour' itself and is a description of what actually happened during the outburst or what the behaviour 'looked' like. The 'C' refers to the 'consequences' of the behaviour – what happened immediately after it – and can include information regarding other people's responses to the behaviour and the eventual outcome for the individual. It can also be a good idea to keep track of where and when the behaviour occurred to assist in identifying any patterns. Here is an example of a completed ABC chart.

For a blank ABC recording sheet you can copy and use to record behaviour, see Appendix 1.

Date and time	Antecedents	Behaviour	Consequences	Other comments
23/8/03 6pm	– Rashid watching Thomas the Tank Engine video in sitting room. – Told to turn off video and come to table for dinner.	Starts screaming and hitting head on floor.	Turns video back on and calms down.	Refused to eat dinner, late to bed.
24/8/03 4pm	– Sister watching TV programme in sitting room. Rashid enters room and puts Thomas video on. – Sister turns video off.	Rashid punches sister.	Sister starts crying and Rashid turns video back on.	
26/8/03 7am	– Getting ready for school. – Asking to watch Thomas video. – Told 'No television before school'.	Starts screaming and hitting mother.	Puts video on and calms down.	Late to school.

Interpreting behavioural records

After recording a number of behavioural incidents, it often becomes possible to see that certain antecedents consistently trigger the behaviour or particular consequences appear to be maintaining it. In the example on page 11, it is clear that Rashid's aggressive outbursts, injuring himself and others, follow situations in which he is unable to access his Thomas the Tank Engine video. In terms of consequences that may maintain the behaviour, we could suggest that Rashid has learned (based on the responses of others) that hitting his head on the floor and lashing out at those thwarting his access to the video are effective ways of ensuring that his needs are met.

In this situation, it would also be important for Rashid's parents to consider the role that the 'obsession' with the Thomas video plays in terms of his ASD. As discussed earlier, many individuals with an ASD have strong interests in particular objects or activities that can have a calming and organizing function in an otherwise often unpredictable world. It is therefore natural that some individuals may become extremely distressed when access to these items or activities is restricted.

Identifying target behaviour and priorities for change: one step at a time

When thinking about addressing any behavioural problem, it is important to select just one or two areas to focus on at a time. Usually they are chosen because they are the types of behaviour that are of most concern or impact most significantly on the individual's life.

There are a number of reasons for this being a good idea. First, homing in on just one or two areas of the behaviour helps us to really understand why it is occurring – what function it serves for the individual and what antecedents or consequences might be involved in triggering and maintaining the behaviour. From this information we can then develop an appropriate intervention or response and measure its effectiveness. Trying to tackle several areas at once can make it very difficult to bring about positive changes in any of them – it's too much to keep track of.

Another important point to remember is that behavioural change takes time. It is unlikely that you will see the results of an intervention immediately – you have to persevere and be patient. Also, and this is key, once an approach is decided on, it is vital that all those in contact with the individual apply it consistently. Everyone involved in the individual's life needs to respond in the same way, every time the behaviour occurs. Being consistent helps them to learn new ways of behaving.

Responding to behavioural difficulties

Once you have identified the factors that may trigger and maintain a particular behaviour and have formed a hypothesis regarding the function of that behaviour for the individual, the next stage is to develop an appropriate intervention.

The important thing to remember here is that the intervention or strategy selected needs to address the root cause or function of the behaviour for the individual if it is to be successful. Which approach is selected will therefore vary according to the individual, to suit them and their unique situation.

The follow pages contain a general overview of some of the strategies that may be used in response to challenging behaviour. For further information regarding a particular approach, please visit the websites of or contact the organizations and companies mentioned or read the books listed in the References and recommended reading section at the back of the booklet.

Preventative or positive strategies

The main focus of any behavioural intervention should always be on the development of new skills to assist the individual in coping with their environment and communicating their needs. To achieve long-lasting behavioural change, it is important to provide them with other ways of achieving the outcome that the behaviour has previously provided.

Improving communication

There is no doubt that difficulties with communication (both expressive and receptive) can be a major factor in relation to many behavioural difficulties for people with ASD. Improving an individual's communication skills (and the way you communicate with them) should therefore be one of the key components of many behavioural interventions.

There are various strategies that can be implemented on a day-to-day basis to improve an individual's ability to communicate with and understand others. Which particular strategies it is best to use will vary according to the individual, but listed below are some examples of approaches that can be helpful.

- Provide as wide a range of communication and social opportunities as possible that are appropriate to the individual.

- Use language that is appropriate to the individual's level of understanding.

- Avoid the use of sarcasm, metaphors and turns of phrase – "I laughed my head off", for example – for those who have a very literal way of interpreting what people say as it can be very confusing and even upsetting.

- Use visual cues – such as objects, pictures, symbols or written instructions – that are appropriate to the individual's level of understanding, to back up verbal information. The use of visual cues is discussed in further detail on the following pages.

- Use concrete terms, particularly with reference to abstract concepts, such as time, and be specific.

- Be positive when providing instructions. Tell the individual what they should be doing rather than what they should not be doing.

- Provide extra thinking time so that information can be processed correctly and use repetition if necessary. Some people with an ASD may process auditory information differently or more slowly than other people. Therefore, it may be necessary to allow extra time for a person with an ASD to respond to a request or question.

On the opposite page is an example of how communication strategies can be effective in addressing a behavioural issue.

Real life example

Kim's teacher observed that, although Kim was one of the stronger students in the class at mathematics, she would often sit at her desk doing nothing after the class had been provided with a set of instructions. The teacher initially thought that Kim was being deliberately obstinate and felt frustrated by her lack of compliance within the classroom.

After speaking with Kim's father and keeping a record of situations where this behaviour occurred, her teacher realized that she responded better when instructions were provided one at a time and if they were broken down into sequential steps and written on the blackboard. Kim's teacher also found it helpful to check with Kim from time to time to ensure that she understood the task and clarify things if she had any questions.

Some individuals with an ASD benefit from the use of augmentative and alternative communication approaches. Some examples of these are as follows.

- Picture symbols with words, printed words or letters and communication boards with photographs, objects or pictures.

- Sign language, such as Makaton. For further information, contact:
  Makaton Vocabulary Development Project (MVDP)
  31 Firwood Drive, Camberley, Surrey GU15 3QD
  Tel: 01276 61390
  Website: www.makaton.org/index.htm
  Email: mvdp@makaton.org

- Object or picture swap systems, such as the Picture Exchange Communication System (PECS). For further information, contact:
  Pyramid Educational Consultants UK Ltd
  Pavilion House, 6 Old Steine, Brighton BN1 1EJ
  Tel: 01273 609555
  Website: www.pecs.org.uk
  Email: pyramid@pecs.org.uk

A speech and language therapist can assist with the assessment of an individual's communication skills and work with you to develop an appropriate programme, which may include the use of an alternative or augmentative communication strategy.

Visual strategies

The value of using visual strategies to assist people on the autistic spectrum to communicate with others and understand their world is widely recognized. People with an ASD tend to process visual information better than verbal information. Using visual cues therefore plays to this strength and may assist them in a number of ways.

Visual cues can be objects, pictures, symbols or words (depending on the individual's level of understanding) and can be implemented in the following ways.

- Visual timetables can be used to indicate what is happening during a morning, day or week. These assist the individual in dealing with difficulties associated with understanding abstract concepts, such as time, sequencing difficulties and anxiety stemming from an inability to imagine what is happening in the future. Visual timetables can take the form of pictures, symbols or words and be broken down as much as is required to reassure the individual. Such timetables can help reduce their anxiety levels and may also promote independence in a number of areas as they are less reliant on prompts from others to complete activities.

- To aid understanding of the concept of 'first…, then', such as 'First you need to have lunch, then you can play outside.'

- As a means of setting up rules for behaviour.

- For communicating physical pain, feelings, wants and needs to others by simply pointing to or showing the relevant symbols.

- They can be used to help individuals make choices between objects or activities.

If you visit the Do to Learn website, you will find further information about the use of visual cues and some free picture symbols.

The address is: **www.dotolearn.com**

Here is an example of how visual cues can be used to address a behavioural difficulty.

Real life example

James loved his swimming lessons, which were held every Tuesday afternoon. However, his parents were finding it increasingly difficult to cope with the constant questioning regarding his next lesson. Each day, James would insist, was swimming day and he would get his swimming costume and towel ready to be taken to his class. Sometimes James would be so distressed when he was informed that he could not swim that day, things would escalate to a full-blown tantrum.

James' parents decided to trial a strategy that his teacher was using with success at school. A weekly timetable was developed that used picture symbols to depict different activities that occurred during the week. The swimming symbol was put in the 'Tuesday' column on the timetable. This was placed on a wall in the kitchen and each time James asked to go swimming, his parents would refer him to his weekly timetable, which would remind him of the day's activities and show him how many days remained until his next swimming class.

After a week of redirecting James to the timetable, the constant questioning gradually reduced and he started referring to the schedule independently. The tantrums also ceased as James could clearly see when he would be able to go swimming again and what activities he would be doing on other days.

Social skills development

Difficulties with social interaction can be a significant cause of problems and distress for people with an ASD. The following are some examples of approaches that can be used to help them to develop skills in this area.

Social skills training

This approach involves directly teaching an individual the skills necessary to cope with social situations and may include instruction on the appropriate use of gestures, eye contact, physical proximity to others, understanding non-verbal communication, appropriate topics for conversation and how to start and end a conversation.

Social skills groups run in some parts of the UK, but not everywhere, so, for further information, contact the Autism Helpline (0845 070 4004, Monday–Friday 10am–4pm or visit www.autism.org.uk or email autismhelpline@nas.org.uk).

Attending such a group can be a good way to develop skills in this area. Alternatively, there are some good books and resources that can help people with an ASD develop social skills (see the References and recommended reading section towards the end of the booklet).

A combination of strategies, including a social skills group, has been used in the example below in order to bring about more acceptable behaviour.

Real life example

Timothy, 15, had started approaching women in public and talking about subjects of a sexual nature – behaviour that had eventually resulted in police involvement. Timothy's parents recognized that the behaviour most likely stemmed from his emerging interest in women and his lack of understanding of socially appropriate ways to approach them.

In addition to enrolling Timothy in a social skills group for adolescents run by their local branch of the NAS, they spent some time developing a list of people in Timothy's life – family, friends, teachers, strangers – and identifying appropriate and inappropriate topics of conversation for each group. Timothy's parents also discussed sex and puberty with him, using pictures and written information to help him understand the changes going on in his body and prepare him for the future.

Social Stories™

Social Stories were developed by Carol Gray in 1991 to help those with an ASD to develop greater social understanding. Each Social Story is a short description of a particular situation, event or activity that includes specific information about what to expect in that situation and why. They can provide an individual with some idea of how others might respond in a particular situation and, therefore, give a framework for appropriate behaviour. Social Stories also enable others to see things from the perspective of the individual with an ASD and why the person may appear to respond or behave in a particular way.

Information on how to write Social Stories can be obtained from Carol Gray's *The New Social Story Book* (1994), which provides detailed information regarding the structure, content and implementation of Social Stories. Further information can also be found at The Gray Center for Social Learning and Understanding's website at www.thegraycenter.org/Social_Stories.htm

In the following example a Social Story provides reassurance.

Real life example

Sinta was terrified of thunder. Whenever the sky was overcast, she would constantly run to the windows to check for lightning and pace the floors, becoming increasingly agitated. During these periods, Sinta would refuse to eat or attend to activities at school. The behaviour was starting to impact her learning and causing great concern to her carers.

Sinta's carers decided to develop a Social Story about thunder. It described what to expect during a thunderstorm and provided Sinta with reassurance that the loud noises, although unpleasant, could not harm her. Sinta's teachers and carers found that, by reading the Social Story together on overcast days, in addition to having a range of activities to hold her attention, Sinta was gradually able to remain calmer during thunder storms.

Circle of Friends and mentoring

Circle of Friends is an approach that was developed by Perske (1988) particularly for school-aged children. It involves identifying a group of peers who are interested in spending time with the person with an ASD and organize for them to actively engage the person in activities during the school day and sometimes also outside of school. Similarly, peer mentors or buddies can facilitate social interaction by modelling appropriate social behaviour and providing support in educational settings or the workplace.

Self-regulation

A skill that it is important for people with an ASD to develop is that of being able to monitor and manage their own behaviour. If an individual can identify and respond appropriately to stressful situations and events, this increases their independence and can also lead to an increased sense of self-efficacy (feelings of confidence and control over own behaviour).

There are several good books available that discuss this area in further detail. *When my Autism Gets Too Big: A Relaxation Book for Children with Autism Spectrum Disorders* by Kari Dunn Buron (2003) and *The Incredible 5-point Scale: Assisting Children with ASDs in Understanding Social Interactions and Controlling their Emotional Responses* by Kari Dunn Buron and Mitzi Curtis (2003) are two books that are designed to help children manage their anxiety levels and work at problem behaviour, such as obsessions. The following are some additional approaches that may assist in the development of self-regulation skills.

Emotions identification training

Many people with an ASD experience difficulties in understanding their own and others' emotions. Emotions training can help by teaching an individual how to read and respond to the cues that represent particular emotions, such as facial expressions and body language, in others and bodily sensations in themselves.

Relaxation

Relaxation approaches – such as deep breathing, thinking positive thoughts, redirection to pleasant, calming activities (such as taking a bath, listening to relaxing music, aromatherapy, playing on a computer, swinging, jumping on a trampoline) – may help an individual with an ASD to manage their anxiety levels and stress.

Real life example

Jennifer always seemed to be in an extremely agitated state on returning home from school in the afternoons. She would often shove furniture around, yell at family members and physically lash out if anyone got too close to her.

Jennifer's mother realized that this was her way of coping with the high stress levels caused by a day of concentration and stimulation at school. She therefore decided to structure a period of relaxation time into Jennifer's schedule on her arrival home.

Jennifer's mother found that 45 minutes alone on her computer after school – an activity Jennifer found to be highly relaxing – was enough to help her calm down and participate in the rest of the evening's activities.

Real life example

David was in his second year of university when he started having problems with his flatmates. Disagreements over minor issues, such as housework or noise levels, often led to major arguments in which David became increasingly agitated – sometimes even destroying property to cope with his frustration. His flatmates were finding it increasingly difficult to cope with his aggressive outbursts and threatened to have him evicted unless he addressed the issue.

David discussed the situation with the student support officer at his university, who arranged a referral to a local counsellor. The counsellor helped David learn to identify the physical signs – fast heartbeat, tense muscles – that indicated he was becoming angry and, together, they developed a plan for how to respond should David find himself in a situation where he felt like this.

David found that walking away from the scene, taking ten deep breaths and spending some time alone in his room helped him to calm down. He also discovered that it was helpful to write down his concerns, then discuss them later with his flatmates as it was easier to express himself clearly when he was feeling calm than when he felt angry. In addition, David's counsellor prepared a list of strategies to assist his flatmates in communicating more effectively with David when dealing with conflict – using clear and concrete language, being specific, raising one concern at a time and so on. This also helped to improve the situation.

Environmental modifications

Creating a well-structured and supportive environment is one of the most effective ways in which to help an individual cope with the difficulties associated with an ASD. The following are some examples of the kinds of environmental modifications that can reduce the likelihood of behavioural difficulties.

Low-arousal environment (physical and social)

The creation of a low-arousal physical and social environment – where sensory stimulation (such as sounds and smells) is minimized – can reduce anxiety and help increase levels of concentration. Scanning the individual's environment for stimuli that they find unpleasant, such as bright lighting, odours, colour, noise levels and clutter, and making reasonable adjustments to minimize the impact of these stimuli can reduce behavioural incidents. It may also be beneficial to set up a relaxation room where the individual can go to escape from a stressful environment or situation and have an opportunity to calm down.

Structuring the environment

Modifying the environment and processes to ensure that the individual with an ASD knows what is going to happen and what is expected of them utilizes the preference for visual organization and can create a sense of order. Examples include setting up visual timetables and using visual cues, creating routines and preplanning for stressful times or events. Communicating what is expected of an individual clearly in terms of their behaviour in a particular environment can also assist in reducing anxiety. Depending on the individual's level of understanding, this may be achieved by means of Social Stories (see page 23) or behavioural contracts (for those at the higher functioning end of the spectrum). Behavioural contracts are written agreements, signed by the individual and another party, that outline the rules and what behaviour is expected of an individual in a particular setting.

Sensory integration strategies

There are several sensory strategies that can be implemented to help individuals cope with their environment. Each person will vary in how exactly they respond to sensory information, so interventions need to be tailored to address that person's specific needs and abilities. The following is an example of how a sensory approach can be an effective way to respond to a behavioural difficulty.

Real life example

Anja would constantly chew on sticks, gravel and rocks that she found in the playground. It was suggested that she enjoyed the sensory experience of chewing on these objects.

Anja's nursery teacher put together some edible alternatives, such as raw pasta and spaghetti, in a bum bag that Anja carried around with her. Her teacher increased supervision of Anja in the playground and redirected her to the items in her bum bag when she reached for inedible items.

Encouraging desirable behaviour

We can encourage the development of new skills and increase the occurrence of appropriate behaviour by changing the way that we respond to them. The following sections suggest a number of approaches that can lead to an increase in preferred behaviour.

Positive reinforcement

Positive reinforcement is the strengthening of a particular behaviour by following it with something desirable. Positive reinforcement should be used as a component in almost all behavioural interventions, to facilitate the development of new skills, encourage appropriate behaviour and enhance self-esteem.

Reinforcers can take a number of different forms, including:

- favourite foods – edibles

- toys or objects – tangibles

- activities

- praise or social reinforcement

- sensory-based reinforcers.

For any of these to lead to an increase in desired behaviour, it is essential that the relevant aspects of the person concerned – their particular preferences, interests and level of ability – are considered first of all. Second, that the reinforcer is something novel – that is, an activity or object that is not readily available. Third, reinforcers need to be changed as often as necessary to ensure that the individual does not tire of them. It is very important, therefore, to have a variety of reinforcers available.

Reinforcement works best when it is provided immediately after the desired behaviour has occurred and when the activity or behaviour that is being encouraged is clearly named. For example, you might say, "That's nice sharing, Jack."

Reinforcement can be provided in a number of ways, depending on what behaviour it is that we are wishing to encourage or discourage. The following are some examples of different ways in which reinforcement can be used to strengthen or weaken particular behaviour.

Real life examples

1. Three-year-old Mohammed constantly climbs on to people's laps rather than sitting on his own chair. His parents provide verbal praise and a tickle each time he sits on his chair independently.

2. Max's hand-flapping behaviour interferes with his ability to concentrate on his schoolwork. His teacher recognizes that the hand-flapping may provide important sensory input for Max, so has devised a programme whereby reinforcement is provided for reduced hand-flapping during periods of deskwork.

3. Jane displays a range of challenging types of behaviour during lunchtimes at school. The members of staff have decided that reducing aggressive behaviour towards other students is a priority and so give Jane positive reinforcement for those periods of time when there is no aggressive behaviour, even though she is still exhibiting other types of undesirable behaviour.

Token systems

For some, the use of token systems can be a very useful way of increasing the occurrence of desired behaviour.

Token systems are a form of positive reinforcement that involve the acquisition of points, ticks, stars, stickers, small objects or symbols. These may not necessarily be inherently reinforcing, but can eventually be exchanged for a positive reinforcer.

Such systems usually work best with higher-functioning individuals who are able to wait for their reward and understand visual symbols. Verbal praise and encouragement should still be provided as the individual achieves each token.

Real life example

Kazuo experienced difficulties getting ready in the mornings and, consequently, was frequently late for school.

Kazuo's father decided to set up a token economy system to correct this. Kazuo earned a sticker on a chart for each step of the morning routine that he completed successfully. If Kazuo completed all the tasks – putting on his clothes, having breakfast, cleaning his teeth, getting his bag ready – he earned 30 extra minutes on his video game machine after school.

Prompting

Prompting is a technique that can help individuals to learn new skills by providing them with the required level of input to complete a task or activity. Prompts can be of the following kinds – in descending order of intrusiveness and level of support provided:

- physical
- gestural
- verbal
- environmental.

Prompting is paired with positive reinforcement (see page 30) to strengthen each stage of learning a particular skill. The ultimate goal is for the individual to be able to complete a task independently, without prompting, so this approach involves gradually reducing the type and level of support provided.

Real life example

Jeremy, who is four years old, was learning to wash his hands independently. Initially, Jeremy's mother found it necessary to physically move his hands on to the tap and turn on the water, wet his hands, use the soap and so on.

Jeremy's mother continued to help him, but paired reinforcement with the physical prompts. She found that, gradually, Jeremy began to learn each stage of the task and do that himself. Eventually, Jeremy's mother was able to stop providing physical prompts and he could complete the activity with occasional verbal prompts only. As time progressed, the verbal prompts were replaced with a series of picture symbols placed on the wall above the bathroom basin, which provided Jeremy with a reminder of each stage of the activity, should he need it.

Shaping

Shaping is the process whereby increasingly closer approximations to the desired response are reinforced.

An example of an activity that shaping can help with is enabling a child to eat independently. Initially in such a situation, reinforcement may need to be provided to the child for reaching for his spoon. Then, once this stage has been mastered, reinforcement is held back until the child actually picks up the spoon and so on until the child is spooning food into his mouth independently.

Chaining

Chaining is the term used for the technique of breaking down an activity into its smaller components (known as task analysis), then the gradual teaching of these successive components in a way suited to the abilities of the individual. There are two types of chaining.

- Forward chaining follows the steps of an activity in the order that they would usually occur. An example would be helping a child learn how to put her trousers on independently by initially teaching her how to put each foot into the trousers, then how to pull the trousers up and, finally, how to do up the zip and button.

- Backward chaining starts with the last component of the activity and works backwards to the beginning. So, for putting on trousers, you would help the child with the first steps – putting her legs into the trousers and pulling them up – then focus on teaching her how to do up the zip and button. Once this last step has been mastered, you would teach her how to pull the trousers up independently, then, finally, how to put her feet into the trouser legs. Despite seeming an unusual way to teach new skills, backward chaining is sometimes preferred to forward chaining if the last stage of the activity is the easiest to learn. Also, it can provide the learner with an increased sense of self-efficacy and achievement as the first stage to be mastered is the completed activity or the 'finished product'.

Negative reinforcement

Negative reinforcement involves the removal of an undesirable situation or activity to strengthen a desirable behaviour. Negative reinforcement is not the same as punishment, as is sometimes thought. Further information regarding punishment can be found later in this booklet.

The following is an example of how negative reinforcement might be used as a strategy for addressing a behavioural issue.

Real life example

Emma, who is 20, dislikes the noise of the television and usually screams until it is turned off. Her carers want to encourage Emma's independence, so teach her the skills needed to turn the television off herself when the noise upsets her.

Instead of responding to Emma's screams, they wait until Emma turns the television off on her own. The ceasing of the noise negatively reinforces the behaviour of Emma turning the television off independently.

General guidelines

Consistency

One of the most important things to bear in mind when undertaking any behavioural strategy or intervention is the need for a consistent approach. Without the support and commitment of all relevant people in the learner's life, it is unlikely that lasting behavioural change will be achieved. If a strategy is proving too difficult to implement consistently, then it is worth going back, reviewing it and making any necessary adjustments.

Generalization

Generalizing new skills that have been learned in a particular situation or environment to other occasions and places where they can also be used is something that frequently presents particular challenges to those with an ASD. It is therefore essential that special care is taken to encourage the person to apply new skills and coping strategies to a variety of environments, not just the one they learned about.

Maintenance

From time to time, it may be necessary to go back and revisit a particular strategy or approach if an individual is experiencing difficulties to ensure that the new skills they learned are maintained over time. This may be particularly necessary around times of illness, stress or change when they might revert to old patterns of behaviour.

Fading out prompts and reinforcers

Our ultimate goal for any behavioural intervention should always be to promote an individual's independence, quality of life and self-efficacy. To this end, it is important that any prompts and reinforcers (with the exception of verbal praise) are gradually reduced to as low a level as possible, while still maintaining the desired behavioural change.

Reactive (management) strategies

In addition to the implementation of proactive or positive behavioural strategies, it is sometimes necessary to have a range of other strategies available in order to respond to a behavioural incident or outburst. These approaches will be referred to as reactive or management strategies in the following section.

None of these techniques should ever be implemented in isolation. Indeed, if it is necessary to use any of them, then a range of positive or proactive strategies should also be implemented on a regular basis.

Extinction (planned ignoring)

Extinction or planned ignoring is a strategy whereby an unwanted behaviour is ignored. It is a useful one to use when the responses of others – such as attention or providing a desired object or activity – appear to be maintaining an unwanted behaviour.

Planned ignoring involves making no response to the behaviour, including verbal comments, body language and facial expressions. However, it does not mean that the individual is ignored. Thus, planned ignoring needs to be coupled with other strategies, such as positive reinforcement, in order to provide the individual with an opportunity to learn alternative ways of achieving a desired outcome. In other words, in order for this strategy to be effective, it is as important to readily respond positively to and reinforce the individual's appropriate behaviour as it is to not respond to inappropriate behaviour.

It is particularly important when implementing this strategy to be consistent. A common tendency when extinction is first tried is for the incidence of the individual's unwanted behaviour to increase before it decreases. This is called an extinction burst and can be seen as the individual saying, "This approach has worked for me before. Maybe I need to try harder to get them to do what I want." Consistency is extremely important at this point as the individual will otherwise learn that repeating this action, perhaps even more frequently, will bring about the desired response and may escalate the behaviour to the same point or further the next time as well.

Extinction can be used with a number of behavioural difficulties, but should not be tried when the behaviour involves the risk of harm to the individual or others, such as self-injurious or aggressive behaviour.

The example overleaf shows planned ignoring helped to reduce a boy's habit of swearing.

Real life example

Mohinder had started swearing at home. He was ten years old. His father observed that this behaviour usually occurred while he was doing his homework and resulted in Mohinder being asked to go to his room for a period of time out. It was becoming clear that Mohinder was using the swearing as a way of avoiding doing his homework.

Mohinder and his father developed a behavioural contract together. It stated that Mohinder agreed to spend 30 minutes working on his homework, after which time he would be able to go to his room. His father also introduced a token economy system, with Mohinder earning points for each ten-minute period during which he did not swear while completing his homework. These he was able to trade in for an agreed reward once he had achieved a certain number of points.

In addition, where he would previously get angry and send Mohinder to his room for a period of time out in response to his swearing, his father started using planned ignoring and, instead of punishing him for doing it, continued to focus instead on the work that they were doing together. Once Mohinder started to see the points accumulate on his chart and realized that the swearing no longer brought about the desired outcome, his swearing gradually became less and less frequent.

Redirection

Redirecting an individual's attention to a preferred topic of conversation or activity can be an extremely effective way of preventing escalation and defusing a difficult situation.

It can be helpful to have a range of calming and distracting activities lined up so that they are ready to use if the individual starts to become agitated. Relaxation strategies and anger management techniques (mentioned earlier under the heading Self-regulation) may be utilized to redirect and refocus an individual who is distressed.

It is useful for the individual and others to be aware of the signs of their distress. These vary from person to person, but can include swearing, pacing, hand biting, talking to themselves. Be ready to redirect the individual's attention to a calming activity when any of these signs are observed.

Time out

This approach involves time out from positive reinforcement, which may or may not involve removing the individual from the environment.

Time out is an appropriate strategy to use at times when you want to address behaviour that is reinforced by factors in the individual's environment. It can also be useful when you need to help an individual de-escalate undesirable behaviour by limiting arousal created by external stimuli.

If a time out area is to be used, it is very important that this be an identified uninteresting space, but one that is safe, so that there is no risk of them harming themselves, and where they can be unobtrusively observed throughout – again, to ensure their safety.

The individual needs to be informed as to why they need to go to the space to have a time out and this should be backed up with visual cues (such as picture symbols or Social Stories) if necessary. Time out should never last longer than a few minutes and any reduction in agitation should be encouraged. Following time out, the individual should then be redirected to a calming, neutral activity and reinforcement provided for the first occurrence of appropriate behaviour.

Responding to crises

Sometimes an individual's behaviour escalates to the point where that person's safety or the safety of others is at risk. This is particularly the case with aggressive and self-injurious behaviour. In these instances, it is important to have a range of strategies that can be implemented to try to defuse the situation and help the person calm down. Being aware of potential triggers and avoiding these as much as possible, as well as watching for indicators that the person is becoming increasingly distressed, can all help in avoiding escalation to a full-blown incident.

Consider the following points and then you can develop a planned response to cope successfully with behavioural outbursts.

- Try to think of triggers (events, situations or things) that could possibly be sparking off behavioural outbursts.

Possible triggers	Strategies to try
• Changes to routine • Medical issues, such as pain or illness • Frustration at communication difficulties • Stressful social situations • Sensory overload.	• Environmental modifications • Use of alternative or argumentative communications strategies, such as signs or picture symbols • Redirection to relaxing, neutral activities • Removal of trigger (or individual) from the environment.

- Look out for cues of distress – signs that the individual is becoming increasingly distressed and building up to a behavioural incident.

Possible cues of distress	Strategies to try
- Facial expressions - Bodily movements or gestures - Repetitive behaviour - Yelling, shouting.	- Responding calmly and clearly - Removing demands - Rewarding and posting up rule reminders – using visual cues to back up the message - Reinforcing calm behaviour - Redirecting to a neutral activity - Removing the individual or others from the environment.

- Note what kinds of behaviour are exhibited during a behavioural incident or crisis.

Possible types of behaviour	Strategies to try
- Aggression towards others - Injuring themselves - Destroying property - Tantrums.	- Responding calmly and clearly - Ensuring that the environment is safe - Removing yourself and others from the environment to ensure your and their safety, while continuing to observe the individual froma distance - Getting extra help, if needed - Providing the minimal response required until individual begins to calm down.

- Think about how to handle the time just after an incident has occurred.

Possible behaviour	Strategies to try
• The behaviour may be reducing in intensity or have ceased, but the person may still be quite agitated or stressed.	• Give the individual space to calm down (hold off on discussions or demands) • Redirect individual to a neutral activity and provide praise for appropriate behaviour • Reinforce calm behaviour • Wait until individual has calmed completely before raising issue (if appropriate) or making demands.

Why punishment does not work

'Punishment' here means the use of aversive (unpleasant) stimuli or withholding normally occurring activities or objects to reduce an undesirable behaviour. Forms of punishment can include:

- smacking, slapping, hitting

- shouting, scolding, yelling

- the use of aversive substances, such as water sprays

- the use of physical restraints.

Much research has been carried out to explore this area and the evidence very clearly suggests that the use of punishment as a response to behavioural difficulties does not work. Here are some of the reasons for this.

- Punishment does not address the root cause or causes of the behaviour. Even if it is effective in reducing one kind of behaviour in the short term, often it will quickly be replaced by another (sometimes even more challenging) kind as the question "Why is this behaviour occurring?" has not been answered.

- Punishment tends to be effective only when it is used in a particular setting and is delivered by a particular individual. This is particularly the case for those with an ASD who experience difficulties generalizing learning across different environments.

- Punishment models a way of behaving for the individual that can cause more problems in the future. For example, smacking a child for a particular behaviour may teach them to treat others in the same way.

- Punishment can lead to aggression towards the person administering it.

- The use of punishment for individuals who have difficulties communicating and relating to others, understanding the world and whose lives are already stressful in many ways raises significant ethical issues (Howlin, 1998a).

Please note: Sometimes the use of physical restraints may be considered necessary in cases of extreme self-injury, but this should always be under the guidance of a qualified specialist (such as a clinical psychologist or psychiatrist) and be considered a last resort response.

When you need help

When to seek professional support

- If an individual's behaviour places them or others at risk, as would be the case with self-injury or aggression towards others.

- If an individual's behaviour is occurring in several environments and they are resistant to intervention.

- If, as a parent or carer, you are finding it difficult to cope with your child's behaviour.

Where and how to get extra help

For more detailed information about professionals who might be able to help with behavioural difficulties in those with an ASD, please ring the Autism Helpline for the information sheet entitled *Who can help? Professionals involved in autism.*

Specialist support

Arrange an appointment with your family GP and request a referral to a specialist with knowledge of ASD and behavioural issues, such as a clinical psychologist, psychiatrist or Behaviour Support Team, if there is one operating in your area.

Arrange an appointment with your GP to specifically discuss behavioural concerns and bring along completed ABC recording sheets (see earlier under the heading Recording behaviour and Appendix 1 for a blank sheet that you can copy and use) or a diary of behavioural incidents. Communicating your concerns regarding your child's behaviour to the GP as clearly as possible is important as then an appropriate referral can be made. If your GP is not aware of appropriate specialists in your area, the following organizations may be able to help.

Autism Helpline
393 City Road, London EC1V 1NG
Tel: 0845 070 4004 (opening hours Monday to Friday 10am–4pm)
Website: www.autism.org.uk
Email: autismhelpline@nas.org.uk

The Autism Helpline holds a database of specialists who have indicated that they have expertise or interest in the area of ASD. This database is not comprehensive (it does not include the details of all specialists across the country) and the Helpline is unable to recommend any particular specialist, but it is able to provide the details of specialists it has listed for different parts of the country if requested.

The British Psychological Society (BPS)
St Andrews House, 48 Princess Road East,
Leicester LE1 7DR
Tel: 0116 254 9568
Website: www.bps.org.uk
Email: enquiry@bps.org.uk

British Association for Counselling and Psychotherapy (BACP)
BACP House, 35–37 Albert Street, Rugby,
Warwickshire CV21 2SG
(The registered office is open Monday to Friday, 8.45am–5pm)
Tel: 0870 443 5252
Website: www.bacp.co.uk
Email: bacp@bacp.co.uk

British Association for Behavioural and Cognitive Psychotherapies (BABCP)
BABCP, The Globe Centre, PO Box 9,
Accrington BB5 0XB
Tel: 01254 875277
Website: www.babcp.com
Email: babcp@babcp.com

Courses and training

Workshops, courses and training opportunities may be another way in which you can increase your understanding of an individual's challenging behaviour. Information regarding forthcoming training opportunities across the country for parents and carers is frequently updated on The National Autistic Society's website at the following link:

www.autism.org.uk/courses

Alternatively, you might like to get in touch with your local society for information about courses in your area. For contact details of your local society or group, please contact the Autism Helpline (details as given on page 49).

If you are the parent or carer of a child who has been newly diagnosed, you might be interested in finding out about The National Autistic Society's EarlyBird Programme (concerning children aged four and under) or *help!* (concerning children aged five and over). Further information regarding these programmes can be obtained by visiting the programmes' websites or contacting them directly:

for the EarlyBird Programme
Jo Stevens, Director, EarlyBird Centre, 3 Victoria Crescent West, Barnsley, South Yorkshire S75 2AE
Tel: 01226 779 218
Website: www.autism.org.uk/earlybird
Email: earlybird@nas.org.uk

for the *help!* programme
help! programme, The National Autistic Society,
Church House, Filton,
Bristol BS34 7BD
Tel: 0117 974 8411
Website: www.autism.org.uk/help!
Email: help.programme@nas.org.uk

The Challenging Behaviour Foundation may be able
to provide information regarding training and
workshop opportunities and it also produces a series
of factsheets discussing a range of behavioural issues.
For further information, contact:

The Challenging Behaviour Foundation
c/o Friends Meeting House, Northgate, Rochester,
Kent ME1 1LS
Tel: 01634 838739
Website: www.thecbf.org.uk
Email: info@thecbf.org.uk

Taking a break

Dealing with challenging behaviour can be highly demanding for parents and carers. All parents need a break from caring for their children from time to time – this is normal and healthy. Making sure that you have the energy to respond appropriately and support an individual with challenging behaviour is one of the most important aspects of any intervention. Thinking about your own needs means that you will be better equipped to provide the best support possible to your child or family member with an ASD.

Support from partners, family, friends or neighbours is important, but help can also be requested from Social Services. The sort of help that might be available will vary depending on the individual and their particular needs, but can include respite care, a home help, funding for equipment or holidays or modifications to your home.

To find out what you are entitled to, write to your local Social Services office and request an assessment of the individual's needs under Section 47 of the *NHS and Community Care Act 1990* for adults or under *Section 17 of the Children Act 1989* for children. You can also request an assessment of your needs as a carer under the *Carers (Recognition and Services) Act 1995* and the *Carers and Disabled Children Act 2000.*

For further information on how to get help from Social Services, contact the Autism Helpline (tel: 0845 070 4004, email: autismhelpline@nas.org.uk).

Further information – Autism Helpline

Some parents find that sharing their experiences with others who have gone through similar things can be a good source of support and information. The National Autistic Society Autism Helpline holds details of parent groups across the country and can put you in touch with your local group if requested. For this and further information contact the Helpline on 0845 070 4004.

References and recommended reading

There are very good books available that provide more information regarding behavioural issues for people with an ASD than it has been possible to explore here. Listed below are some that you should find helpful. Books available from The National Autistic Society's Publications Catalogue are marked with a star. To find out details of the books' distributors, please contact The National Autistic Society's Publications Department on 020 7903 3595.

Adams, Janice (1995). *Autism – PDD: creative ideas during the school years.* Ontario: Adams Publications

*Attwood, Tony (1998). *Asperger syndrome: a guide for parents and professionals.* London: Jessica Kingsley

*Clements, John, and Zarkowska, Eva (2000). *Behavioural concerns and autistic spectrum disorders: explanations and strategies for change.* London: Jessica Kingsley

*Dunn Buron, K. (2003). *When my autism gets too big: a relaxation book for children with autism spectrum disorders.* Sawnee Mission, Kansas: Autism Asperger Publishing Company

*Dunn Buron, K., and Curtis, M. (2003). *The incredible 5-point scale: assisting children with ASDs in understanding social interactions and controlling their emotional responses.* Shawnee Mission, Kansas: Autism Asperger Publishing Company

Fouse, B., and Wheeler, M. (1997). *A treasure chest of behavioural strategies for individuals with autism.* Arlington, Texas: Future Horizons

Gray, C. (ed.) (1994). *The new Social Story book.* Arlington, Texas: Future Horizons

*Gray, C. (2002). *My Social Stories book.* London: Jessica Kingsley

*Hannah, Liz (2001). *Teaching young children with autistic spectrum disorders to learn.* Norwich: The National Autistic Society

Happe, Francesca (1994). *Autism: an introduction to psychological theory.* London: UCL Press

Howlin, Patricia (1998a). *Children with autism and Asperger syndrome: a guide for practitioners and carers.* Chichester: John Wiley & Sons

Howlin, Patricia (1998). 'Autism', in P. Howlin (ed.), *Behavioural approaches to problems in childhood.* Cambridge: Cambridge University Press

Keenan, M., Kerr, K. P., and Dillenburger, K. (2000). *Parents' education as autism therapists: applied behaviour analysis in context.* London: Jessica Kingsley

*Leicester City Council and Leicestershire County Council (1998). *Asperger syndrome: practical strategies for the classroom: a teacher's guide.* London: The National Autistic Society

*Leicestershire County Council and Fosse Health Trust (1998) *Autism: how to help your young child.* London: The National Autistic Society

Perske, R. (1988). *Circle of friends.* Nashville, Tennessee: Abingdon Press

Schopler, Eric (ed.) (1995). *Parent survival manual.* New York: Plenum

*The National Autistic Society (1998). *The autistic spectrum: a parent's guide.* London: The National Autistic Society

*Whitaker, Philip (2001). *Challenging behaviour and autism: making sense – making progress.* London: The National Autistic Society

Willis, Thomas J., LaVigna, Gary, W., and Donnellan, Anne M. (1993). *Behaviour assessment guide.* Los Angeles, California: Institute for Applied Behavior Analysis

*Wing, Lorna (1996). *The autistic spectrum: a guide for parents and professionals.* London: Constable

Appendix 1

ABC behaviour record sheet

Date and time	Antecedents	Behaviour	Consequences	Other comments

Index